M000098810

YOUR
PRETTYPENNIES

The Ultimate Financial Planner: Create, Plan, and Achieve Your Financial Goals During The Next Twelve Months

Created By:
Tara Jones, Financial Coach & Educator

It is our mission to reach as many individuals and assist in their financial transformations. Share your experience using The Ultimate Financial Planner with others by posting your photos using the hashtag #yourprettypennies on any social media platform.

To reorder The Ultimate Financial Planner and to browse other financial products, visit www.yourprettypennies.com.
This book is also available through Amazon.

Copyright © 2016 by Tara Jones
All rights reserved.

No part of this planner may be reproduced, distributed, or transmitted in any form or by any means, including photocopying, recording, or other electronic or mechanical methods, without prior written permission of the creator.

This Financial Planner Belongs To:

If Found, Call The Following Number:

On this _____ day of _____, 20___,
I, _____, commit to using this financial planner for the next twelve months to create monthly budgets, track monthly spending, record payment due dates, and follow my debt repayment plan to achieve the financial goals I have set.

Financial success is attainable and can only be achieved by setting financial goals that you are passionate about and are committed to. You now have a tool that will house these goals and serve as a constant reminder of your commitment. Starting and ending your month with The Ultimate Financial Planner will empower you manage your money with intention and enable you to reach your goals.

The Ultimate Financial Planner is a fail-proof financial goal-setting system created with you in mind. Now, I say it's fail-proof not because an error isn't possible (no one can predict the future or control all circumstances), but because if you follow this plan, from month one to twelve, you will accomplish more than you would with any other method you have tried this far. It is not exclusive to any one type of financial situation, which means it will work for you. Your numbers are different from the next person, but the process you need to achieve your goals are not.

As a Financial Coach and Educator, I love assisting women with becoming financially stable so they can build wealth and design their desired lifestyles. I create processes, products, and services with the objective of moving them to their next financial level.

In creating this financial gem, I have taken the guesswork out of what it takes for you to achieve your short-term and long-term financial goals within the next twelve months. If you set your goals, make a plan, get to work, and stick to it, I have no doubts that you will reach them.

Wishing you much success on this journey.

All The Best,

Tara J.

You Are The Root
of Your Financial
Success or Failure.

If You Work On
The Roots, The Fruits
of Your Work
Will Grow.

How To

Financial Goals Template

The Financial Goals template allows you to
set two financial goals for the next twelve months –
one short-term and one long-term. The short-term goal should be accomplished within
six months. The long-term goal should be accomplished within twelve months. Do not
set more than two financial goals within a twelve-month period because you are likely
to set goals in other areas of your life. Setting too many goals for yourself this year wil
cause overwhelm and eventually you will disconnect from them. Once you established
two financial goals, set 3 subgoals for each that will lead you to accomplish them.

I highly recommend using the S.M.A.R.T. goal-setting method to create financial goals
that are specific, measurable, actionable (sub goals), realistic, and time-sensitive.
Here's an example:

*I will save $5,000 in my emergency fund savings account during the next twelve
months.*

Subgoal #1: I will save $417 per month for 12 months. ($417 x 12 = $5,004)
*Subgoal #2: I will set up an automatic payment transfer of $417 from my checking
account to savings account on the 12th of each month.*
*Subgoal #3: I will temporarily cancel my gym membership and begin to weekly meal
prep so I can comfortably save $417 per month.*

Note: Your financial goals should be reflected in your monthly budget.

Debt Repayment Plan Template

The Debt Repayment Plan template offers you a space to record your current debts
and to create a repayment process. Choose whether to pay off debt beginning with the
lowest payment amount or the highest interest rate. There are advantages to both
methods so choose based on what works best for you. By paying off debt from the
lowest payment to the highest, you will constantly gain quick wins during this process -
which is needed to stay the course. If you choose to begin by paying off the debt with
the largest interest rate first, you will pay less interest over time - which is also
advantageous.

Keep in mind that your repayment plan will only work if you commit to keeping your
monthly expense amount lower than your monthly income amount. If you are spending
more (or as much) than you make each month, you will not have money to put toward
the debt. You should resolve this issue before beginning your debt repayment plan.
Also, establish a small emergency fund savings of $2,000 to cover any unforeseen
expenses while you are working your plan.

Due Dates

The Due Dates template allows you to record and track your monthly expenses so you will never miss a payment again. Simply fill in the numerical dates and the name and amount of each expense on the calendar template.

Bonus: A Financial Goal section has been provided for you to write out which subgoal(s) you will focus on each month. You could also record a mini goal for yourself in that space. Here's an example: *"I will meal plan weekly to eliminate the cost of dining out from my budget."*

Monthly Budget

The Monthly Budget template will assit you in using your current income to achieve your financial goals during the next twelve months. This simple, zero-based budget allows you to effectively allocate 100% of your monthly income to your expenses and financial goals. Creating a budget each and every month is vital to financial success so do not skip this template.

Monthly Expense Tracker

Use the Monthly Expense Tracker template to record and analyze your spending habits each month. It will help you identify which payment method (cash, credit, or debit) you use when you making small and large purchases. It also reveals where, when, and how you spend your money so you can determine ways to scale back and spend wisely as you work towards achieving your financial goals.

Goal Check

The Goal Check template is designed to help you evaluate your progress in achieving your financial goals during the next twelve months. A major part of the financial goal-setting process is setting aside time to reflect on points of success and failure, which can be applied or avoided in the upcoming months.

Affirm Yourself

The Affirm Yourself Page allows you to freewrite five money affirmations. They are essential to the process of achieving short-term and long-term goals. Every three months, record five and declare them as often as needed.

FINANCIAL GOALS

SHORT TERM GOAL

_____

ACTIONABLE SUBGOALS

_____

_____

_____

WHY THIS GOAL IS IMPORTANT TO ME

_____

_____

_____

LONG TERM GOAL

_____

ACTIONABLE SUBGOALS

_____

_____

_____

WHY THIS GOAL IS IMPORTANT TO ME

_____

_____

_____

DEBT REPAYMENT PLAN

1. Decide whether you will be paying off your debts from *smallest balance to largest balance* or *highest interest rate to lowest interest rate*.

2. Using the table below, fill in the name of the **company**, **interest rate**, **current balance**, and **minimum payment amount** for each debt.

3. Create this month's zero-based budget on Pages 12 and 13.
   - Determine your disposable income amount (the amount of money you have left after your monthly expenses are covered).
   - Under the Debts Category, fill in "Debt Repayment Plan" next to "Other:" and add in the disposable income amount.

4. In the table below, enter in the **disposable income amount** for the first debt.

5. Calculate the **total monthly payment** by adding the minimum payment amount to the disposable income amount.

6. Each month, pay minimum payments on the other debts listed plus at least the total monthly payment on the first debt until it is paid in full.

7. When the first debt is **paid in full**, write the date of last payment in the table below.

8. Begin the process of paying off the next debt using Steps 3 through 7.
   Note: Your disposable income amount should increase because you have one less monthly minimum payment in your budget.

9. Repeat this debt repayment process until you have paid all debts in full.

10. Celebrate! This is a major achievement.

COMPANY	INTEREST RATE	CURRENT BALANCE	MINIMUM PAYMENT AMOUNT	DISPOSABLE INCOME AMOUNT	TOTAL MONTHLY PAYMENT	PAID IN FULL

Due Dates

MONTH:

SUNDAY	MONDAY	TUESDAY	WEDNESDAY	THURSDAY	FRIDAY	SATURDAY

Financial Goal For This Month:

Financial Freedom Is Not A Sprint...It's A Marathon.

MONTHLY EXPENSE TRACKER

DATE	CATEGORY	PURCHASE DESCRIPTION	AMOUNT	CASH/CREDIT/DEBIT	NEED VS. WANT

MONTHLY BUDGET

INCOME:

INCOME	DATE PAID	AMOUNT
Company:		
Freelance Work:		
Other:		
Total		

EXPENSES:

GIVING	DATE PAID	AMOUNT
Tithing:		
Charity:		
Total (*10-15%)		

SAVINGS ACCOUNTS	DATE PAID	AMOUNT
Emergency Fund:		
Savings Account:		
Retirement:		
Other:		
Total (*10-15%)		

HOUSING	DATE PAID	AMOUNT
Rent/Mortgage:		
Maintenance/Repairs:		
Property Taxes:		
Other:		
Total (*25-35%)		

HOUSEHOLD BILLS / UTILITIES	DATE PAID	AMOUNT
Electricity:		
Gas:		
Water:		
Cable:		
Internet:		
Mobile Phone:		
Cleaning Services:		
Other:		
Total (*5-10%)		

FOOD	DATE PAID	AMOUNT
Groceries:		
Dining Out:		
Total (*5-15%)		

TRANSPORTATION	DATE PAID	AMOUNT
Car Fuel:		
Maintenance/Repairs:		
Public Transportation:		
Other:		
Total (*10-15%)		

CLOTHING	DATE PAID	AMOUNT
Personal:		
Child(ren):		
Dry Cleaning/Laundry:		
Other:		
Total (*2-7%)		

MEDICAL	DATE PAID	AMOUNT
Physician:		
Dentist:		
Eye Doctor:		
Other:		
Total (*5-10%)		

INSURANCE	DATE PAID	AMOUNT
Health:		
Renter/Homeowner:		
Auto:		
Other:		
Total (*10-25%)		

PERSONAL	DATE PAID	AMOUNT
Gym Membership:		
Toiletries:		
Hair Salon/Barber Shop:		
Childcare/Nanny:		
Allowances/Spending Money:		
Miscellaneous:		
Other:		
Total (*5-10%)		

RECREATION	DATE PAID	AMOUNT
Social Events/Conferences:		
Hobbies:		
Personal Development Materials:		
Extra-Curricular Activities:		
Other:		
Total (*5-10%)		

DEBTS	DATE PAID	AMOUNT
Auto Loan:		
Student Loan:		
Student Loan:		
Credit Card:		
Credit Card:		
Credit Card:		
Personal Loan:		
Personal Loan:		
Other:		
Other:		
Total (*5-10%)		

*Suggested percentage of income

Total Income	
− Category Totals	
= Zero Balance	

Due Dates

MONTH:

SUNDAY	MONDAY	TUESDAY	WEDNESDAY	THURSDAY	FRIDAY	SATURDAY

Financial Goal For This Month:

Budget Monthly.

MONTHLY EXPENSE TRACKER

DATE	CATEGORY	PURCHASE DESCRIPTION	AMOUNT	CASH/CREDIT/DEBIT	NEED VS. WANT

MONTHLY BUDGET

INCOME:

INCOME	DATE PAID	AMOUNT
Company:		
Freelance Work:		
Other:		
Total		

EXPENSES:

GIVING	DATE PAID	AMOUNT
Tithing:		
Charity:		
Total (*10-15%)		

SAVINGS ACCOUNTS	DATE PAID	AMOUNT
Emergency Fund:		
Savings Account:		
Retirement:		
Other:		
Total (*10-15%)		

HOUSING	DATE PAID	AMOUNT
Rent/Mortgage:		
Maintenance/Repairs:		
Property Taxes:		
Other:		
Total (*25-35%)		

HOUSEHOLD BILLS / UTILITIES	DATE PAID	AMOUNT
Electricity:		
Gas:		
Water:		
Cable:		
Internet:		
Mobile Phone:		
Cleaning Services:		
Other:		
Total (*5-10%)		

FOOD	DATE PAID	AMOUNT
Groceries:		
Dining Out:		
Total (*5-15%)		

TRANSPORTATION	DATE PAID	AMOUNT
Car Fuel:		
Maintenance/Repairs:		
Public Transportation:		
Other:		
Total (*10-15%)		

CLOTHING	DATE PAID	AMOUNT
Personal:		
Child(ren):		
Dry Cleaning/Laundry:		
Other:		
Total (*2-7%)		

MEDICAL	DATE PAID	AMOUNT
Physician:		
Dentist:		
Eye Doctor:		
Other:		
Total (*5-10%)		

INSURANCE	DATE PAID	AMOUNT
Health:		
Renter/Homeowner:		
Auto:		
Other:		
Total (*10-25%)		

PERSONAL	DATE PAID	AMOUNT
Gym Membership:		
Toiletries:		
Hair Salon/Barber Shop:		
Childcare/Nanny:		
Allowances/Spending Money:		
Miscellaneous:		
Other:		
Total (*5-10%)		

RECREATION	DATE PAID	AMOUNT
Social Events/Conferences:		
Hobbies:		
Personal Developnent Materials:		
Extra-Curricular Activities:		
Other:		
Total (*5-10%)		

DEBTS	DATE PAID	AMOUNT
Auto Loan:		
Student Loan:		
Student Loan:		
Credit Card:		
Credit Card:		
Credit Card:		
Personal Loan:		
Personal Loan:		
Other:		
Other:		
Total (*5-10%)		

*Suggested percentage of income

	Total Income
−	Category Totals
=	Zero Balance

Due Dates

MONTH:

SUNDAY	MONDAY	TUESDAY	WEDNESDAY	THURSDAY	FRIDAY	SATURDAY

Financial Goal For This Month:

Pay Your Bills On Time...
Everytime.

MONTHLY EXPENSE TRACKER

DATE	CATEGORY	PURCHASE DESCRIPTION	AMOUNT	CASH/CREDIT/DEBIT	NEED VS. WANT

MONTHLY BUDGET

INCOME:

INCOME	DATE PAID	AMOUNT
Company:		
Freelance Work:		
Other:		
Total		

EXPENSES:

GIVING	DATE PAID	AMOUNT
Tithing:		
Charity:		
Total (*10-15%)		

SAVINGS ACCOUNTS	DATE PAID	AMOUNT
Emergency Fund:		
Savings Account:		
Retirement:		
Other:		
Total (*10-15%)		

HOUSING	DATE PAID	AMOUNT
Rent/Mortgage:		
Maintenance/Repairs:		
Property Taxes:		
Other:		
Total (*25-35%)		

HOUSEHOLD BILLS / UTILITIES	DATE PAID	AMOUNT
Electricity:		
Gas:		
Water:		
Cable:		
Internet:		
Mobile Phone:		
Cleaning Services:		
Other:		
Total (*5-10%)		

FOOD	DATE PAID	AMOUNT
Groceries:		
Dining Out:		
Total (*5-15%)		

TRANSPORTATION	DATE PAID	AMOUNT
Car Fuel:		
Maintenance/Repairs:		
Public Transportation:		
Other:		
Total (*10-15%)		

CLOTHING	DATE PAID	AMOUNT
Personal:		
Child(ren):		
Dry Cleaning/Laundry:		
Other:		
Total (*2-7%)		

MEDICAL	DATE PAID	AMOUNT
Physician:		
Dentist:		
Eye Doctor:		
Other:		
Total (*5-10%)		

INSURANCE	DATE PAID	AMOUNT
Health:		
Renter/Homeowner:		
Auto:		
Other:		
Total (*10-25%)		

PERSONAL	DATE PAID	AMOUNT
Gym Membership:		
Toiletries:		
Hair Salon/Barber Shop:		
Childcare/Nanny:		
Allowances/Spending Money:		
Miscellaneous:		
Other:		
Total (*5-10%)		

RECREATION	DATE PAID	AMOUNT
Social Events/Conferences:		
Hobbies:		
Personal Developnent Materials:		
Extra-Curricular Activities:		
Other:		
Total (*5-10%)		

DEBTS	DATE PAID	AMOUNT
Auto Loan:		
Student Loan:		
Student Loan:		
Credit Card:		
Credit Card:		
Credit Card:		
Personal Loan:		
Personal Loan:		
Other:		
Other:		
Total (*5-10%)		

*Suggested percentage of income

	Total Income
−	Category Totals
=	Zero Balance

Goal Check

MONTH 3

1.) What subgoals did I accomplish in the last three months?

2.) What financial challenges did I experience in the last three months?

3.) What should be my next specific action to achieve the other subgoals?

Moment of Gratitude

What am I thankful for, despite my current financial situation?

Affirm Yourself:

Freewrite 5 Money Affirmtions In The Blank Space Below.

Due Dates

MONTH:

SUNDAY	MONDAY	TUESDAY	WEDNESDAY	THURSDAY	FRIDAY	SATURDAY

Financial Goal For This Month:

Your Future Self Is Thanking You. Keep Going!

MONTHLY EXPENSE TRACKER

DATE	CATEGORY	PURCHASE DESCRIPTION	AMOUNT	CASH/CREDIT/DEBIT	NEED VS. WANT

MONTHLY BUDGET

INCOME:

INCOME	DATE PAID	AMOUNT
Company:		
Freelance Work:		
Other:		
Total		

EXPENSES:

GIVING	DATE PAID	AMOUNT
Tithing:		
Charity:		
Total (*10-15%)		

SAVINGS ACCOUNTS	DATE PAID	AMOUNT
Emergency Fund:		
Savings Account:		
Retirement:		
Other:		
Total (*10-15%)		

HOUSING	DATE PAID	AMOUNT
Rent/Mortgage:		
Maintenance/Repairs:		
Property Taxes:		
Other:		
Total (*25-35%)		

HOUSEHOLD BILLS / UTILITIES	DATE PAID	AMOUNT
Electricity:		
Gas:		
Water:		
Cable:		
Internet:		
Mobile Phone:		
Cleaning Services:		
Other:		
Total (*5-10%)		

FOOD	DATE PAID	AMOUNT
Groceries:		
Dining Out:		
Total (*5-15%)		

TRANSPORTATION	DATE PAID	AMOUNT
Car Fuel:		
Maintenance/Repairs:		
Public Transportation:		
Other:		
Total (*10-15%)		

CLOTHING	DATE PAID	AMOUNT
Personal:		
Child(ren):		
Dry Cleaning/Laundry:		
Other:		
Total (*2-7%)		

MEDICAL	DATE PAID	AMOUNT
Physician:		
Dentist:		
Eye Doctor:		
Other:		
Total (*5-10%)		

INSURANCE	DATE PAID	AMOUNT
Health:		
Renter/Homeowner:		
Auto:		
Other:		
Total (*10-25%)		

PERSONAL	DATE PAID	AMOUNT
Gym Membership:		
Toiletries:		
Hair Salon/Barber Shop:		
Childcare/Nanny:		
Allowances/Spending Money:		
Miscellaneous:		
Other:		
Total (*5-10%)		

RECREATION	DATE PAID	AMOUNT
Social Events/Conferences:		
Hobbies:		
Personal Developnent Materials:		
Extra-Curricular Activities:		
Other:		
Total (*5-10%)		

DEBTS	DATE PAID	AMOUNT
Auto Loan:		
Student Loan:		
Student Loan:		
Credit Card:		
Credit Card:		
Credit Card:		
Personal Loan:		
Personal Loan:		
Other:		
Other:		
Total (*5-10%)		

*Suggested percentage of income

	Total Income
−	Category Totals
=	Zero Balance

Due Dates

MONTH:

SUNDAY	MONDAY	TUESDAY	WEDNESDAY	THURSDAY	FRIDAY	SATURDAY

Financial Goal For This Month:

If You Will Be Broke After Buying It, You Can't Afford It.

MONTHLY EXPENSE TRACKER

DATE	CATEGORY	PURCHASE DESCRIPTION	AMOUNT	CASH/CREDIT/DEBIT	NEED VS. WANT

MONTHLY BUDGET

INCOME:

INCOME	DATE PAID	AMOUNT
Company:		
Freelance Work:		
Other:		
Total		

EXPENSES:

GIVING	DATE PAID	AMOUNT
Tithing:		
Charity:		
Total (*10-15%)		

SAVINGS ACCOUNTS	DATE PAID	AMOUNT
Emergency Fund:		
Savings Account:		
Retirement:		
Other:		
Total (*10-15%)		

HOUSING	DATE PAID	AMOUNT
Rent/Mortgage:		
Maintenance/Repairs:		
Property Taxes:		
Other:		
Total (*25-35%)		

HOUSEHOLD BILLS / UTILITIES	DATE PAID	AMOUNT
Electricity:		
Gas:		
Water:		
Cable:		
Internet:		
Mobile Phone:		
Cleaning Services:		
Other:		
Total (*5-10%)		

FOOD	DATE PAID	AMOUNT
Groceries:		
Dining Out:		
Total (*5-15%)		

TRANSPORTATION	DATE PAID	AMOUNT
Car Fuel:		
Maintenance/Repairs:		
Public Transportation:		
Other:		
Total (*10-15%)		

CLOTHING	DATE PAID	AMOUNT
Personal:		
Child(ren):		
Dry Cleaning/Laundry:		
Other:		
Total (*2-7%)		

MEDICAL	DATE PAID	AMOUNT
Physician:		
Dentist:		
Eye Doctor:		
Other:		
Total (*5-10%)		

INSURANCE	DATE PAID	AMOUNT
Health:		
Renter/Homeowner:		
Auto:		
Other:		
Total (*10-25%)		

PERSONAL	DATE PAID	AMOUNT
Gym Membership:		
Toiletries:		
Hair Salon/Barber Shop:		
Childcare/Nanny:		
Allowances/Spending Money:		
Miscellaneous:		
Other:		
Total (*5-10%)		

RECREATION	DATE PAID	AMOUNT
Social Events/Conferences:		
Hobbies:		
Personal Development Materials:		
Extra-Curricular Activities:		
Other:		
Total (*5-10%)		

DEBTS	DATE PAID	AMOUNT
Auto Loan:		
Student Loan:		
Student Loan:		
Credit Card:		
Credit Card:		
Credit Card:		
Personal Loan:		
Personal Loan:		
Other:		
Other:		
Total (*5-10%)		

*Suggested percentage of income

	Total Income
−	Category Totals
=	Zero Balance

Due Dates

MONTH:

SUNDAY	MONDAY	TUESDAY	WEDNESDAY	THURSDAY	FRIDAY	SATURDAY

Financial Goal For This Month:

"If At First You Don't Succeed, Dust Yourself Off And Try Again."

MONTHLY EXPENSE TRACKER

DATE	CATEGORY	PURCHASE DESCRIPTION	AMOUNT	CASH/CREDIT/DEBIT	NEED VS. WANT

MONTHLY BUDGET

INCOME:

INCOME	DATE PAID	AMOUNT
Company:		
Freelance Work:		
Other:		
Total		

EXPENSES:

GIVING	DATE PAID	AMOUNT
Tithing:		
Charity:		
Total (*10-15%)		

SAVINGS ACCOUNTS	DATE PAID	AMOUNT
Emergency Fund:		
Savings Account:		
Retirement:		
Other:		
Total (*10-15%)		

HOUSING	DATE PAID	AMOUNT
Rent/Mortgage:		
Maintenance/Repairs:		
Property Taxes:		
Other:		
Total (*25-35%)		

HOUSEHOLD BILLS / UTILITIES	DATE PAID	AMOUNT
Electricity:		
Gas:		
Water:		
Cable:		
Internet:		
Mobile Phone:		
Cleaning Services:		
Other:		
Total (*5-10%)		

FOOD	DATE PAID	AMOUNT
Groceries:		
Dining Out:		
Total (*5-15%)		

TRANSPORTATION	DATE PAID	AMOUNT
Car Fuel:		
Maintenance/Repairs:		
Public Transportation:		
Other:		
Total (*10-15%)		

CLOTHING	DATE PAID	AMOUNT
Personal:		
Child(ren):		
Dry Cleaning/Laundry:		
Other:		
Total (*2-7%)		

MEDICAL	DATE PAID	AMOUNT
Physician:		
Dentist:		
Eye Doctor:		
Other:		
Total (*5-10%)		

INSURANCE	DATE PAID	AMOUNT
Health:		
Renter/Homeowner:		
Auto:		
Other:		
Total (*10-25%)		

PERSONAL	DATE PAID	AMOUNT
Gym Membership:		
Toiletries:		
Hair Salon/Barber Shop:		
Childcare/Nanny:		
Allowances/Spending Money:		
Miscellaneous:		
Other:		
Total (*5-10%)		

RECREATION	DATE PAID	AMOUNT
Social Events/Conferences:		
Hobbies:		
Personal Develpment Materials:		
Extra-Curricular Activities:		
Other:		
Total (*5-10%)		

DEBTS	DATE PAID	AMOUNT
Auto Loan:		
Student Loan:		
Student Loan:		
Credit Card:		
Credit Card:		
Credit Card:		
Personal Loan:		
Personal Loan:		
Other:		
Other:		
Total (*5-10%)		

*Suggested percentage of income

	Total Income
−	Category Totals
=	Zero Balance

Goal Check

MONTH 6

1.) What subgoals did I accomplish in the last three months?

2.) What financial challenges did I experience in the last three months?

3.) What should be my next specific action to achieve the other subgoals?

Moment of Gratitude

What am I thankful for, despite my current financial situation?

Affirm Yourself:

Freewrite 5 Money Affirmtions In The Blank Space Below.

Due Dates

MONTH:

SUNDAY	MONDAY	TUESDAY	WEDNESDAY	THURSDAY	FRIDAY	SATURDAY

Financial Goal For This Month:

Your Financial Plan Will Not Work Unless You Do!

MONTHLY EXPENSE TRACKER

DATE	CATEGORY	PURCHASE DESCRIPTION	AMOUNT	CASH/CREDIT/DEBIT	NEED VS. WANT

MONTHLY BUDGET

INCOME:

INCOME	DATE PAID	AMOUNT
Company:		
Freelance Work:		
Other:		
Total		

EXPENSES:

GIVING	DATE PAID	AMOUNT
Tithing:		
Charity:		
Total (*10-15%)		

SAVINGS ACCOUNTS	DATE PAID	AMOUNT
Emergency Fund:		
Savings Account:		
Retirement:		
Other:		
Total (*10-15%)		

HOUSING	DATE PAID	AMOUNT
Rent/Mortgage:		
Maintenance/Repairs:		
Property Taxes:		
Other:		
Total (*25-35%)		

HOUSEHOLD BILLS / UTILITIES	DATE PAID	AMOUNT
Electricity:		
Gas:		
Water:		
Cable:		
Internet:		
Mobile Phone:		
Cleaning Services:		
Other:		
Total (*5-10%)		

FOOD	DATE PAID	AMOUNT
Groceries:		
Dining Out:		
Total (*5-15%)		

TRANSPORTATION	DATE PAID	AMOUNT
Car Fuel:		
Maintenance/Repairs:		
Public Transportation:		
Other:		
Total (*10-15%)		

CLOTHING	DATE PAID	AMOUNT
Personal:		
Child(ren):		
Dry Cleaning/Laundry:		
Other:		
Total (*2-7%)		

MEDICAL	DATE PAID	AMOUNT
Physician:		
Dentist:		
Eye Doctor:		
Other:		
Total (*5-10%)		

INSURANCE	DATE PAID	AMOUNT
Health:		
Renter/Homeowner:		
Auto:		
Other:		
Total (*10-25%)		

PERSONAL	DATE PAID	AMOUNT
Gym Membership:		
Toiletries:		
Hair Salon/Barber Shop:		
Childcare/Nanny:		
Allowances/Spending Money:		
Miscellaneous:		
Other:		
Total (*5-10%)		

RECREATION	DATE PAID	AMOUNT
Social Events/Conferences:		
Hobbies:		
Personal Development Materials:		
Extra-Curricular Activities:		
Other:		
Total (*5-10%)		

DEBTS	DATE PAID	AMOUNT
Auto Loan:		
Student Loan:		
Student Loan:		
Credit Card:		
Credit Card:		
Credit Card:		
Personal Loan:		
Personal Loan:		
Other:		
Other:		
Total (*5-10%)		

*Suggested percentage of income

	Total Income
−	Category Totals
=	Zero Balance

Due Dates

MONTH:

SUNDAY	MONDAY	TUESDAY	WEDNESDAY	THURSDAY	FRIDAY	SATURDAY

Financial Goal For This Month:

Create Wealth By Saving More & Spending Less.

MONTHLY EXPENSE TRACKER

DATE	CATEGORY	PURCHASE DESCRIPTION	AMOUNT	CASH/CREDIT/DEBIT	NEED VS. WANT

MONTHLY BUDGET

INCOME:

INCOME	DATE PAID	AMOUNT
Company:		
Freelance Work:		
Other:		
Total		

EXPENSES:

GIVING	DATE PAID	AMOUNT
Tithing:		
Charity:		
Total (*10-15%)		

SAVINGS ACCOUNTS	DATE PAID	AMOUNT
Emergency Fund:		
Savings Account:		
Retirement:		
Other:		
Total (*10-15%)		

HOUSING	DATE PAID	AMOUNT
Rent/Mortgage:		
Maintenance/Repairs:		
Property Taxes:		
Other:		
Total (*25-35%)		

HOUSEHOLD BILLS / UTILITIES	DATE PAID	AMOUNT
Electricity:		
Gas:		
Water:		
Cable:		
Internet:		
Mobile Phone:		
Cleaning Services:		
Other:		
Total (*5-10%)		

FOOD	DATE PAID	AMOUNT
Groceries:		
Dining Out:		
Total (*5-15%)		

TRANSPORTATION	DATE PAID	AMOUNT
Car Fuel:		
Maintenance/Repairs:		
Public Transportation:		
Other:		
Total (*10-15%)		

CLOTHING	DATE PAID	AMOUNT
Personal:		
Child(ren):		
Dry Cleaning/Laundry:		
Other:		
Total (*2-7%)		

MEDICAL	DATE PAID	AMOUNT
Physician:		
Dentist:		
Eye Doctor:		
Other:		
Total (*5-10%)		

INSURANCE	DATE PAID	AMOUNT
Health:		
Renter/Homeowner:		
Auto:		
Other:		
Total (*10-25%)		

PERSONAL	DATE PAID	AMOUNT
Gym Membership:		
Toiletries:		
Hair Salon/Barber Shop:		
Childcare/Nanny:		
Allowances/Spending Money:		
Miscellaneous:		
Other:		
Total (*5-10%)		

RECREATION	DATE PAID	AMOUNT
Social Events/Conferences:		
Hobbies:		
Personal Development Materials:		
Extra-Curricular Activities:		
Other:		
Total (*5-10%)		

DEBTS	DATE PAID	AMOUNT
Auto Loan:		
Student Loan:		
Student Loan:		
Credit Card:		
Credit Card:		
Credit Card:		
Personal Loan:		
Personal Loan:		
Other:		
Other:		
Total (*5-10%)		

*Suggested percentage of income

	Total Income
−	Category Totals
=	Zero Balance

Due Dates

MONTH:

SUNDAY	MONDAY	TUESDAY	WEDNESDAY	THURSDAY	FRIDAY	SATURDAY

Financial Goal For This Month:

Your Net-Worth Does Not Equal Your Self-Worth.

MONTHLY EXPENSE TRACKER

DATE	CATEGORY	PURCHASE DESCRIPTION	AMOUNT	CASH/CREDIT/DEBIT	NEED VS. WANT

MONTHLY BUDGET

INCOME:

INCOME	DATE PAID	AMOUNT
Company:		
Freelance Work:		
Other:		
Total		

EXPENSES:

GIVING	DATE PAID	AMOUNT
Tithing:		
Charity:		
Total (*10-15%)		

SAVINGS ACCOUNTS	DATE PAID	AMOUNT
Emergency Fund:		
Savings Account:		
Retirement:		
Other:		
Total (*10-15%)		

HOUSING	DATE PAID	AMOUNT
Rent/Mortgage:		
Maintenance/Repairs:		
Property Taxes:		
Other:		
Total (*25-35%)		

HOUSEHOLD BILLS / UTILITIES	DATE PAID	AMOUNT
Electricity:		
Gas:		
Water:		
Cable:		
Internet:		
Mobile Phone:		
Cleaning Services:		
Other:		
Total (*5-10%)		

FOOD	DATE PAID	AMOUNT
Groceries:		
Dining Out:		
Total (*5-15%)		

TRANSPORTATION	DATE PAID	AMOUNT
Car Fuel:		
Maintenance/Repairs:		
Public Transportation:		
Other:		
Total (*10-15%)		

CLOTHING	DATE PAID	AMOUNT
Personal:		
Child(ren):		
Dry Cleaning/Laundry:		
Other:		
Total (*2-7%)		

MEDICAL	DATE PAID	AMOUNT
Physician:		
Dentist:		
Eye Doctor:		
Other:		
Total (*5-10%)		

INSURANCE	DATE PAID	AMOUNT
Health:		
Renter/Homeowner:		
Auto:		
Other:		
Total (*10-25%)		

PERSONAL	DATE PAID	AMOUNT
Gym Membership:		
Toiletries:		
Hair Salon/Barber Shop:		
Childcare/Nanny:		
Allowances/Spending Money:		
Miscellaneous:		
Other:		
Total (*5-10%)		

RECREATION	DATE PAID	AMOUNT
Social Events/Conferences:		
Hobbies:		
Personal Development Materials:		
Extra-Curricular Activities:		
Other:		
Total (*5-10%)		

DEBTS	DATE PAID	AMOUNT
Auto Loan:		
Student Loan:		
Student Loan:		
Credit Card:		
Credit Card:		
Credit Card:		
Personal Loan:		
Personal Loan:		
Other:		
Other:		
Total (*5-10%)		

*Suggested percentage of income

−	Total Income
	Category Totals
=	Zero Balance

Goal Check

MONTH 9

1.) What subgoals did I accomplish in the last three months?

2.) What financial challenges did I experience in the last three months?

3.) What should be my next specific action to achieve the other subgoals?

Moment of Gratitude

What am I thankful for, despite my current financial situation?

Affirm Yourself:

Freewrite 5 Money Affirmtions In The Blank Space Below.

Due Dates

MONTH:

SUNDAY	MONDAY	TUESDAY	WEDNESDAY	THURSDAY	FRIDAY	SATURDAY

Financial Goal For This Month:

Review Your Monthly Bank Statements.

MONTHLY EXPENSE TRACKER

DATE	CATEGORY	PURCHASE DESCRIPTION	AMOUNT	CASH/CREDIT/DEBIT	NEED VS. WANT

MONTHLY BUDGET

INCOME:

INCOME	DATE PAID	AMOUNT
Company:		
Freelance Work:		
Other:		
Total		

EXPENSES:

GIVING	DATE PAID	AMOUNT
Tithing:		
Charity:		
Total (*10-15%)		

SAVINGS ACCOUNTS	DATE PAID	AMOUNT
Emergency Fund:		
Savings Account:		
Retirement:		
Other:		
Total (*10-15%)		

HOUSING	DATE PAID	AMOUNT
Rent/Mortgage:		
Maintenance/Repairs:		
Property Taxes:		
Other:		
Total (*25-35%)		

HOUSEHOLD BILLS / UTILITIES	DATE PAID	AMOUNT
Electricity:		
Gas:		
Water:		
Cable:		
Internet:		
Mobile Phone:		
Cleaning Services:		
Other:		
Total (*5-10%)		

FOOD	DATE PAID	AMOUNT
Groceries:		
Dining Out:		
Total (*5-15%)		

TRANSPORTATION	DATE PAID	AMOUNT
Car Fuel:		
Maintenance/Repairs:		
Public Transportation:		
Other:		
Total (*10-15%)		

CLOTHING	DATE PAID	AMOUNT
Personal:		
Child(ren):		
Dry Cleaning/Laundry:		
Other:		
Total (*2-7%)		

MEDICAL	DATE PAID	AMOUNT
Physician:		
Dentist:		
Eye Doctor:		
Other:		
Total (*5-10%)		

INSURANCE	DATE PAID	AMOUNT
Health:		
Renter/Homeowner:		
Auto:		
Other:		
Total (*10-25%)		

PERSONAL	DATE PAID	AMOUNT
Gym Membership:		
Toiletries:		
Hair Salon/Barber Shop:		
Childcare/Nanny:		
Allowances/Spending Money:		
Miscellaneous:		
Other:		
Total (*5-10%)		

RECREATION	DATE PAID	AMOUNT
Social Events/Conferences:		
Hobbies:		
Personal Development Materials:		
Extra-Curricular Activities:		
Other:		
Total (*5-10%)		

DEBTS	DATE PAID	AMOUNT
Auto Loan:		
Student Loan:		
Student Loan:		
Credit Card:		
Credit Card:		
Credit Card:		
Personal Loan:		
Personal Loan:		
Other:		
Other:		
Total (*5-10%)		

*Suggested percentage of income

	Total Income
−	Category Totals
=	Zero Balance

Due Dates

MONTH:

SUNDAY	MONDAY	TUESDAY	WEDNESDAY	THURSDAY	FRIDAY	SATURDAY

Financial Goal For This Month:

Whatever Your Income Is, Live 20 - 30% Below It.

MONTHLY EXPENSE TRACKER

DATE	CATEGORY	PURCHASE DESCRIPTION	AMOUNT	CASH/CREDIT/DEBIT	NEED VS. WANT

MONTHLY BUDGET

INCOME:

INCOME	DATE PAID	AMOUNT
Company:		
Freelance Work:		
Other:		
Total		

EXPENSES:

GIVING	DATE PAID	AMOUNT
Tithing:		
Charity:		
Total (*10-15%)		

SAVINGS ACCOUNTS	DATE PAID	AMOUNT
Emergency Fund:		
Savings Account:		
Retirement:		
Other:		
Total (*10-15%)		

HOUSING	DATE PAID	AMOUNT
Rent/Mortgage:		
Maintenance/Repairs:		
Property Taxes:		
Other:		
Total (*25-35%)		

HOUSEHOLD BILLS / UTILITIES	DATE PAID	AMOUNT
Electricity:		
Gas:		
Water:		
Cable:		
Internet:		
Mobile Phone:		
Cleaning Services:		
Other:		
Total (*5-10%)		

FOOD	DATE PAID	AMOUNT
Groceries:		
Dining Out:		
Total (*5-15%)		

TRANSPORTATION	DATE PAID	AMOUNT
Car Fuel:		
Maintenance/Repairs:		
Public Transportation:		
Other:		
Total (*10-15%)		

CLOTHING	DATE PAID	AMOUNT
Personal:		
Child(ren):		
Dry Cleaning/Laundry:		
Other:		
Total (*2-7%)		

MEDICAL	DATE PAID	AMOUNT
Physician:		
Dentist:		
Eye Doctor:		
Other:		
Total (*5-10%)		

INSURANCE	DATE PAID	AMOUNT
Health:		
Renter/Homeowner:		
Auto:		
Other:		
Total (*10-25%)		

PERSONAL	DATE PAID	AMOUNT
Gym Membership:		
Toiletries:		
Hair Salon/Barber Shop:		
Childcare/Nanny:		
Allowances/Spending Money:		
Miscellaneous:		
Other:		
Total (*5-10%)		

RECREATION	DATE PAID	AMOUNT
Social Events/Conferences:		
Hobbies:		
Personal Development Materials:		
Extra-Curricular Activities:		
Other:		
Total (*5-10%)		

DEBTS	DATE PAID	AMOUNT
Auto Loan:		
Student Loan:		
Student Loan:		
Credit Card:		
Credit Card:		
Credit Card:		
Personal Loan:		
Personal Loan:		
Other:		
Other:		
Total (*5-10%)		

*Suggested percentage of income

	Total Income
−	Category Totals
=	Zero Balance

Due Dates

MONTH:

SUNDAY	MONDAY	TUESDAY	WEDNESDAY	THURSDAY	FRIDAY	SATURDAY

Financial Goal For This Month:

Celebrate Your Financial Wins!

MONTHLY EXPENSE TRACKER

DATE	CATEGORY	PURCHASE DESCRIPTION	AMOUNT	CASH/CREDIT/DEBIT	NEED VS. WANT

MONTHLY BUDGET

INCOME:

INCOME	DATE PAID	AMOUNT
Company:		
Freelance Work:		
Other:		
Total		

EXPENSES:

GIVING	DATE PAID	AMOUNT
Tithing:		
Charity:		
Total (*10-15%)		

SAVINGS ACCOUNTS	DATE PAID	AMOUNT
Emergency Fund:		
Savings Account:		
Retirement:		
Other:		
Total (*10-15%)		

HOUSING	DATE PAID	AMOUNT
Rent/Mortgage:		
Maintenance/Repairs:		
Property Taxes:		
Other:		
Total (*25-35%)		

HOUSEHOLD BILLS / UTILITIES	DATE PAID	AMOUNT
Electricity:		
Gas:		
Water:		
Cable:		
Internet:		
Mobile Phone:		
Cleaning Services:		
Other:		
Total (*5-10%)		

FOOD	DATE PAID	AMOUNT
Groceries:		
Dining Out:		
Total (*5-15%)		

TRANSPORTATION	DATE PAID	AMOUNT
Car Fuel:		
Maintenance/Repairs:		
Public Transportation:		
Other:		
Total (*10-15%)		

CLOTHING	DATE PAID	AMOUNT
Personal:		
Child(ren):		
Dry Cleaning/Laundry:		
Other:		
Total (*2-7%)		

MEDICAL	DATE PAID	AMOUNT
Physician:		
Dentist:		
Eye Doctor:		
Other:		
Total (*5-10%)		

INSURANCE	DATE PAID	AMOUNT
Health:		
Renter/Homeowner:		
Auto:		
Other:		
Total (*10-25%)		

PERSONAL	DATE PAID	AMOUNT
Gym Membership:		
Toiletries:		
Hair Salon/Barber Shop:		
Childcare/Nanny:		
Allowances/Spending Money:		
Miscellaneous:		
Other:		
Total (*5-10%)		

RECREATION	DATE PAID	AMOUNT
Social Events/Conferences:		
Hobbies:		
Personal Develpoment Materials:		
Extra-Curricular Activities:		
Other:		
Total (*5-10%)		

DEBTS	DATE PAID	AMOUNT
Auto Loan:		
Student Loan:		
Student Loan:		
Credit Card:		
Credit Card:		
Credit Card:		
Personal Loan:		
Personal Loan:		
Other:		
Other:		
Total (*5-10%)		

*Suggested percentage of income

	Total Income
−	Category Totals
=	Zero Balance

MONTH 12

Congratulations! You have made it through twelve months of consistent financial planning. And you've likely gone through a noticeable financial transformation. It is now time to look at your results, reflect back on this journey and note the many ways you have improved in regards to managing your money. Identifying the challenges and setbacks you have faced during the last twelve months is also important and should be noted.

To share your financial success story, post your photos on social media using the hashtag #yourprettypennies. Also, please take a moment and review The Ultimate Financial Planner on Amazon.

To reorder this planner so you can achieve another set of financial goals in next 12 months, visit www.yourprettypennies.com.

Results:

How much debt did I pay off in the last twelve months?

How much money have I saved in the last twelve months?

What goals from the Financial Goals sheet did I accomplish?

If I did not achieve my goals, what should I do differently next time?

What was the biggest problem I faced over the last twelve months and how did I overcome it?

What breakthroughs did I make in my finances in the last twelve months?

What new financial habits did I cultivate in the last twelve months?

What was my most common mental state during this financial journey (e.g. excited, proud, stressed)?

What single achievement am I the most proud of?

How did my overall outlook on money management evolve?

ACCOUNT INFORMATION

CHECKING ACCOUNT INFORMATION

Bank / Credit Union:
Phone Number:
Address:

Account Number:
Routing Number:

Online Banking Website:
Username:
Password:

Notes:

SAVINGS ACCOUNT INFORMATION

Bank / Credit Union:
Phone Number:
Address:

Account Number:
Routing Number:

Online Banking Website:
Username:
Password:

Notes:

RETIREMENT ACCOUNT INFORMATION

Bank / Credit Union:
Phone Number:
Address:

Account Number:
Routing Number:

Online Banking Website:
Username:
Password:

Notes:

ACCOUNT INFORMATION

CHECKING ACCOUNT INFORMATION

Bank / Credit Union:
Phone Number:
Address:

Account Number:
Routing Number:

Online Banking Website:
Username:
Password:

Notes:

SAVINGS ACCOUNT INFORMATION

Bank / Credit Union:
Phone Number:
Address:

Account Number:
Routing Number:

Online Banking Website:
Username:
Password:

Notes:

RETIREMENT ACCOUNT INFORMATION

Bank / Credit Union:
Phone Number:
Address:

Account Number:
Routing Number:

Online Banking Website:
Username:
Password:

Notes:

Notes:

_____
_____
_____
_____
_____
_____
_____
_____
_____
_____
_____
_____
_____
_____
_____
_____
_____
_____
_____

Notes:

_____

_____

_____

_____

_____

_____

_____

_____

_____

_____

_____

_____

_____

_____

_____

_____

_____

_____

_____

Made in the USA
Middletown, DE
25 April 2021

38177475R10040